METRO

OFFICIAL HAN

Researched and written by Eric Ogden and John Senior with the co-operation and on behalf of GMPTE and GMML. Authors and Publisher also acknowledge considerable assistance and encouragement from GMA and its sub-contractors.
© Transport Publishing Company Limited, September 1991.
Second Impression November 1991.

Produced for Transport Publishing Company Limited : Glossop : Derbyshire
by Mopok Graphics, 128 Pikes Lane, Glossop, Derbyshire
Designed by Janine Booth

CONTENTS

FOREWORD
by Councillor Jack Flanagan

Metrolink would not have been possible without the wholehearted support of the ten city and borough councils of Greater Manchester. They have contributed financially to the system and all believe that progress has to be made in public transport.

Light Rapid Transit is obviously the way forward. We are most grateful that all political parties, the Greater Manchester Development Corporation, the Chambers of Trade and Commerce and many others have supported us in our endeavours to bring this most modern system to Greater Manchester.

We are more than confident that the system will have the necessary support of the travelling public.

More than 40 other cities throughout the country seek to emulate us in planning and building Light Rapid Transit systems.

As a Mancunian I am obviously delighted that not only Greater Manchester but so many other cities will look upon Metrolink in future years as the obvious choice to improving public transport.

We aim, through the system, to reduce car use and traffic congestion. Metrolink will contribute greatly to reducing pollution and improving the general quality of our surroundings.

INTRODUCTION

It may be useful to start by answering some questions which most people interested in Metrolink will be asking:-

What is Metrolink?

Metrolink is a Light Rapid Transit system — LRT for short — and as such uses electrically-powered light rail vehicles, sometimes referred to as Supertrams, running on steel rails and providing a quick, comfortable, easy-accessible means of public transport. Over 300 such systems operate throughout the world and visitors to the continent of Europe can hardly fail to notice that most progressive cities incorporate a form of LRT as part of their corporate traffic strategy.

Manchester is far from unique in suffering worsening traffic congestion. The increase in numbers of motor cars seeking or needing access to city centres has been recognised as a world-wide problem for many years but Manchester will be Britain's first city to tackle the problem head on and to make a major investment in modern on-street light rail public transport.

The United Kingdom has long since fallen behind its continental neighbours in the areas of priority and investment for public transport. Only two LRT systems have been built in Britain, one on Tyneside, opened in 1980, and the other in London's Docklands, opened in 1987, though neither of these systems uses on-street operation. We should not forget Blackpool of course, where electric street tramways began in this country in 1885, and where modern tramcars still work alongside older models to move vast numbers of holiday makers. But Blackpool is the sole mainland survivor of the previous era whilst Manchester is set to be the first of the new generation.

Light Rail operation in many European towns and cities provides fast, comfortable, efficient transport directly into the commercial centre — as here in Berne. Metrolink will do this in Manchester.

Why is Metrolink right for Manchester, and what will it achieve ?

We firmly believe, and have convinced Government — itself no mean achievement — that Metrolink is right for the Greater Manchester area. Historically Manchester has always suffered from having no rail connection between its main line railway stations, and the ever increasing congestion in the city streets makes for an awkward and time-consuming interchange. This is reflected in increased costs for businesses and also shows itself when shoppers prefer to use other towns where there is less congestion and parking is easier and sometimes cheaper. If the city is to retain its commercial prominence as the regional centre this trend must be reversed.

Metrolink, with an interchange directly below Piccadilly railway station, and linked to Victoria and Deansgate stations, also on the British Rail network, will provide easy and fast access between these points. It will also give access right to the heart of the shopping and business centre, with on-street stations at High Street, Market Street, Mosley Street, St Peter's Square and the G-Mex Exhibition Centre. From G-Mex the LRT cars (LRVs) will travel to Altrincham, using the former British Rail line with which it connects in a £6m junction at Cornbrook. From Victoria the LRVs will travel to Bury, again using the former British Rail railway line, though in this case much work will have been done to provide the overhead catenary for the electric vehicles. At Bury and Altrincham the PTE has already provided Bus Interchanges to facilitate travel to and from Manchester.

City planners have calculated that whereas there were some 53,000 vehicles penetrating the central core of the city in 1985 that figure will rise to 74,000 by the year 2005 unless action is taken now.

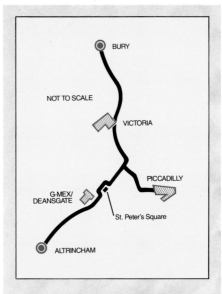

The diagram above shows how Metrolink has linked the two former British Rail lines from Altrincham and Bury to Manchester. The section between G-Mex, Piccadilly and Victoria stations will be the first new generation on-street Light Rail operation in Britain.

The diagram below, prepared by the Manchester City Engineer's department, illustrate the City's commitment to reducing the number of vehicles entering the City. Metrolink is expected to play its part by making public transport more attractive and thereby weaning motorists out of their cars and onto the new Light Rail Vehicles. Park and Ride facilities will be part of this strategy but the development of the Metrolink network to cater for other areas is crucial if a major reduction is to be achieved.

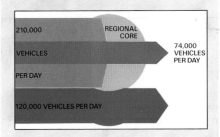

The inner ring road has been designed to take away one third of the through traffic, as shown in the accompanying diagram, and Metrolink will form another essential part of the traffic strategy in the city.

Motor traffic will be re-routed where necessary to ensure that the Metrolink — and also the buses serving the city centre — have priority, thus reducing delays to a minimum and giving better service to a higher percentage of the travelling public. These traffic improvements are part of the on-going commitment by the City Engineer and Surveyor, with whom we work very closely, to reduce the number of cars entering the city, and improved public transport is crucial to this objective.

Commuters and shoppers using Metrolink will be encouraged to leave their cars at out-of-town stations where car parks are being created or extended, and the fast, clean, attractive modern LRVs will undoubtedly enhance the quality of travel. Experience on every modern LRT system demonstrates that significant increases in the number of passengers using the system will quickly occur — increases of up to 40% in three years are quite normal.

Businesses will also benefit from Metrolink; already property developers are promoting the advantages of 'being close to the Metrolink system' and shops will also see the benefits accruing from easier access for their customers. Great care has gone into the design of cars and station platforms to give easy access for those with push chairs or in wheelchairs. This will create a much needed improvement, and one that we know from our researches will be much appreciated. The reduction in numbers of motor cars will also benefit pedestrians through lower exhaust levels in the city.

For all these and many other reasons we expect to see the environmentally friendly Metrolink system, with its quiet cars running on track specially insulated to minimise noise levels, playing a vital role in regenerating the city centre. Electrical operation means that on-street pollution by the LRVs will be minimal.

How have we achieved its creation?

How we have achieved all this can only be briefly covered in this handbook, though a more comprehensive volume is being produced for those who wish to find out more of the answers. The Greater Manchester Passenger Transport Executive — owner of the Metrolink system — is charged with the task of overseeing the provision and improving public transport within Greater Manchester and is responsible to local government, who monitor its progress. It is noteworthy that all ten district councils in the Manchester area saw the value of Metrolink and all have worked together, through the Passenger Transport Authority — which sets public transport policy — harmoniously to achieve its creation.

At the time the PTA and PTE were set up in 1969 the Selnec Transportation Study was on the point of recommending a full-sized railway tunnel under the city centre linking Piccadilly and Victoria stations — the PiccVic scheme. (The Study had investigated numerous alternative cross-city connections, including an early proposal for a heavy rapid transit line linking Ringway with Langley across the city centre.)

A great deal of work was put into the PiccVic scheme and, indeed, Parliamentary Powers were obtained. However, Government funding was refused in 1973 and the scheme formally abandoned in 1977.

In 1982 the PTE, together with the former Greater Manchester Council and BR, mounted a joint study into the connurbation's rail network with special

The Project Light Rail demonstration at Manchester's Debdale Park in March 1987 gave LRT a timely boost, and allowed people to see just what it could offer to local commuters. Credit for this initiative goes to GEC Transportation Projects, Balfour Beatty Power Construction, Fairclough Civil Engineering, British Rail Engineering and British Rail London Midland Region who arranged the event and operated a London Dockland Light Railway car along a stretch of disused railway line. Transport Minister David Mitchell waves the flag as the car prepares to make its inaugural trip.

reference to those parts of the network that were diesel-operated or where the infrastructure was in need of wholesale renewal. Having looked at numerous alternatives a light rail network consisting of a six-line system focussed on a common central section showed the most promising option. Clearly it would have to be built in phases and the linking of the Bury and Altrincham lines was to be the first phase.

A detailed specification was drawn up and further work was carried out by the PTE on its feasibilty and viability. On the strength of these reports the PTE was able to present its case to the Department of Transport for Government authority to proceed, and for assistance with funding.

In order to qualify for grant aid, without which the £112m scheme could not have proceeded, it was necessary to demonstrate that LRT would benefit all the community, not just those who would travel on it. Amongst other criteria it was a stipulation that for every £1 invested in the scheme there should be a benefit, or return, in excess of that amount. Latest figures for Metrolink in Manchester show that the financial return on every pound invested will be in excess of £2.30.

The Government accepted the PTE's proposals subject to a single contract being let to the Private Sector for the designing, building, operating and maintaining (DBOM) of the system. The PTE prepared a Reference Specification and this was put out to Tender as described later in this book. The principal contractors — The GMA Consortium — undertook the DBOM responsibility.

A contract of this size involves hundreds of organisations, generating work for a large number of people. It is not possible to record all the companies involved in the space available but GEC Alsthom and Mowlem, builders of the London Docklands LRT system, are the principal contractors along with the AMEC Group. The fourth member of the Consortium, Greater Manchester Buses Ltd, will be able to provide operating experience. Mott MacDonald assisted the PTE from 1982 by providing Consultancy Services whilst the

Consortium has engaged W. S. Atkins to design the system. Balfour Beatty, a company with worldwide railway building experience and currently involved in the Channel Tunnel project is prominent among the sub-contractors. The latter company is to build the Supertram system in Sheffield, with work beginning later this year, but I am pleased that their work in Manchester will result in our LRVs running first!

The LRVs are being built by Firema in Italy and will be of a new design specially for Manchester. No British company would bid to produce the 26 articulated sets of cars in the time available and at a competitive price. GEC Alsthom who are responsible for this part of the contract are, however, producing the electrical equipment in their Trafford Park and Preston factories, and other companies will be producing components in the UK which will be sent out to Italy to be incorporated in the finished vehicles.

Another notable import is the striking bowstring bridge adjacent to G-Mex and crossing Great Bridgewater Street. Mowlem, which is responsible for civil engineering works including the refurbishment of the existing but long-disused viaduct leading into G-Mex (the former Central Station), used a Belgian company for the manufacture and erection of this latest landmark in the city.

Mowlem is also converting a portion of the area below Piccadilly station — the Undercroft — to become a self-contained two-platform station with lifts and escalators giving access to the main line station concourse.

There are, at the present time in the United Kingdom, over forty-eight towns and cities preparing cases for LRT systems and many of them have sent representatives to Manchester 'to see how it was being done'. I would be less than honest if I did not tell you that in many cases we have advised them that the way we have been obliged by the Department of Transport to go about some aspects of the scheme was not necessarily the best or most cost effective, and we have been able to recommend more advantageous alternatives. This is, of course, the price one pays for being the first but I am sure that our Metrolink system will be second to none and a major asset to the City of Manchester.

David Graham CBE FCA FCIT
Director General
Greater Manchester PTE

Mr Graham, seen below with Secretary of State for Transport Cecil Parkinson, died in April 1991 shortly after writing this Introduction. Metrolink will be a living memorial to his achievements.

CONCEPT TO TENDER

Following some six years of proposals, discussions, visits to other systems, negotiations with British Rail, meetings with the City Engineers and the Police, the local District Councils, and, not least, the Department of Transport, Greater Manchester PTE eventually obtained Government approval in January 1988 to go out to Tender for the construction of the first phase of its Metrolink system.

It will be appreciated that only the biggest — and best — companies in the business would be competent, or financially strong enough, to take on such a project. One of the first things the PTE had to establish was whether those who would seek to build the system did in fact meet such criteria.

What may not perhaps be appreciated is the enormous amount of preparatory work, and the cost of that work, which was necessary. Greater Manchester PTE estimates it had spent over £2m in such work, including consultancy fees, before it could seek tenders for the construction. The City has spent some £⅓m in planning, design approval and supervision to co-ordinate Metrolink into its traffic strategy, with a further £7m spent on moving the statutory services such as gas, electricity, water, sewage, telephone cables and the like which it had been agreed should be moved away from the Metrolink tracks to avoid future disruption of the Light Rail service.

GMA — the successful consortium which is building the system — estimates that its own costs to investigate, prepare design proposals and costings and submit these in the form of Tenders cost hundreds of thousands of pounds, with similar costs to reach the second stage. It should not be forgotten that all work was speculative — those who tendered unsuccessfully must have incurred similar costs. Legal fees for preparation of contracts were considerable.

From these figures it will be appreciated that a very large amount of time and money needs to be spent — it only becomes an investment if the scheme comes to fruition — long before any construction work can begin. Manchester's proposal was unique in many ways, and as such had no precedent for reference. Nevertheless it is the firm and stated belief of many of the parties concerned that Government seriously under-estimated the magnitude and cost of this work, and indeed it admitted to being surprised that so few tenders were received.

The detailed method of submitting tenders, examining and considering the documents and then receiving presentations from those who were seeking to gain the contract was extremely time consuming. It was a vital part of the process and one which, with hindsight, needed even more time and resources than it was possible to make available in order to ensure that all parties' interests were fully considered and adequately covered by the Contract.

The preparation of the legal documentation was also an extremely time-consuming and very expensive business. The contracts formed a pile of paper some 30ins. deep and, as recorded elsewhere, took several hours to sign.

Because the whole process was so complicated, and yet is so interesting, it may now be useful to recap somewhat.

During the early years of the proposals the PTE expected that it would be responsible for the creation and operation of any light rail scheme in Manchester. Its very raison d'etre was to provide and improve transport in Greater Manchester and it alone would have the resources outlined above to investigate and initiate such a scheme.

By the time these proposals were ready to submit to Government the privatisation which had become such a cornerstone of Conservative policy had created a different situation. No longer was the PTE responsible for operation of buses in Greater Manchester, and no longer did it have power to determine fares, service arrangements or to ensure co-ordination.

Neither was it to be allowed to proceed with the funding of the Metrolink project as it would have done prior to the deregulation of bus services in October 1986 and subsequent privatisation. The rules had been changed and it is believed that time will show that these changes have considerably increased the cost of the scheme and its complexity.

In essence the crucial change which occurred was that the Government now required the light rail scheme to be funded by the private sector, and not from public money as would previously have been the case. Whatever the merits or otherwise of such a policy the results were to be far reaching.

It became a condition of Government approval that private industry should design, build, operate and maintain the system. (This has passed into transport terminology as DBOM.) Since the contractors were now being required to take the risks which might arise in the venture, and since they would rightly also need to generate profits for their shareholders, it may be fairly assumed that the costs would not be reduced by such a requirement. It may also be fairly assumed that normal commercial considerations such as any private consortium would need to apply would perhaps not create exactly what the PTE had in mind when it made its original proposals and submitted them to Government since the PTE, at that time, was empowered to subsidise public transport services in Greater Manchester. It is now only empowered to subsidise local rail services and some specified bus services. No general subsidy can be given to Metrolink.

It was necessary for the PTE and the Consortium to reach agreement on the best way of meeting the Government requirement since without it there would be no Metrolink.

Another vital factor was the financing of the £112m project. The Government had indicated that it would meet 50% of the costs (after the private sector contribution) if the scheme met its criteria for a grant under Section 56 of the Transport Act of 1968, but without this grant the scheme would not be able to proceed.

Accordingly the Consortium and PTE prepared the massive documentation which eventually formed the Contract. There were so many documents that the signing alone took some 12 hours! Because there was so much documentation it was impossible to wait for it all to be completed and signed, and construction began 6 months before the Contracts were signed. Had this not been done Metrolink would have been delayed by at least 6 months.

Perhaps future light rail proposals for other towns and cities obliged to follow DBOM requirements will benefit from the Manchester Experience — at least the scale of the operation is now very clearly recognised (and one hopes understood) by both parties — and GMPTE has been able to warn others of the many pitfalls. Indeed they believe that in this instance what Manchester does today the rest of the country should NOT do tomorrow!

THE CONTRACT & THE SUCCESSFUL CONSORTIUM

On 27th September 1989, Greater Manchester Passenger Transport Authority, composed of elected members from each of the ten district authorities of the Greater Manchester region, awarded a contract to the GMA Consortium for the design, building, operation and maintenance of the Greater Manchester Metrolink project, subject to the final approval of the Department of Transport.

The concept of compiling a single contract to design, build, operate and maintain (DBOM) a light rail transit system is unique in Great Britain. Then the method of funding a passenger transportation contract from a partnership of Government and private capital is entirely new. This means that Manchester will have the first of a new generation of British light rail schemes including street running, which, at the present time, about forty British towns and cities will hope to follow.

The DBOM form of contract evolved after long consultations between the PTA and PTE and the Department of Transport, and provided for all the assets to remain in the ownership of the PTE. The Project Group of the PTE was charged with the responsibility for the tendering and evaluation of the Metrolink project.

The press announcement inviting 'suitable interested companies' to apply for inclusion on a selected list of tenderers was made in May 1988. From over one hundred information packs issued, some twelve consortia emerged as likely contenders to be considered for a Stage 1 tender listing and of these eight were selected. To ensure a common briefing all eight were invited on 27th September 1988 to a presentation by the PTE on the tendering process and to receive the Stage 1 tender documentation.

During the Stage 1 tender period detailed discussions were held with the bidders, all questions and answers being logged to ensure that no later misunderstandings arose. During this period, three consortia withdrew and five tenders were received and opened on 1st February 1989. The process included consideration by a number of consultants and liaison with the Department of Transport, the Manchester City Engineer, British Rail and the Statutory Undertakers, responsible for gas, electricity, water and sewerage.

The tender evaluation was considered over four key elements, namely financial, contractual, operational and technical, for each of which a ranking order was produced. An overall assessment was achieved by bringing these together to form a final matrix which provided the basis for three bidders to go forward to Stage 2. The three consortia recommended by the Project Group to proceed to the second stage of tendering were GMA Group, Norwest Holst/Hawker Siddeley and Trafalgar House/BREL, and the recommendations were accepted by the PTA and PTE.

For Stage 2 of the tender process the three consortia received additional data bank information together with updated tender documentation, and they submitted their completed tenders in July 1989. As at Stage 1 the evaluation reports were submitted to the PTA and PTE, both giving approval to the recommendation that the GMA Consortium should be invited to undertake the Manchester Metrolink Project.

On 24th October 1989, the then Minister of State for Transport, Mr Michael Portillo announced that a grant under Section 56 of the Transport Act of 1968 would be available for the project, thus enabling the contract with the GMA Consortium to proceed. The formal signing took place on 6th June 1990, itself a significant date and recalling the opening of the original City tramway system on 6th June 1901.

The contract is, in fact, in several parts which resulted in the signing session continuing into the night. All the elements of a Design, Build, Operate and Maintain contract between a PTE and a newly-established consortium, together with a funding package made up of elements from Central Government, the PTA and the contracting consortium added to the complexity of this unique form of contract.

The successful tenderer was initially known as the GMA Group, consisting of GEC Alsthom Transportation Projects Ltd, John Mowlem & Company PLC, and AMEC plc. GEC Alsthom was responsible directly or through its sub-contractors for the vehicles, the power supply system, signalling, tele-communications and the fare and ticketing systems. Similarly Mowlem carried out, or sub-contracted, the constructional work on the Cornbrook Viaduct, the G-Mex Viaduct and bowstring arch bridge over Great Bridgewater Street, and civil and building work on the stations, together with the construction of the city centre track and alignment. AMEC, through its subsidiary Fairclough Civil Engineering Ltd, constructed the Operations and Maintenance Centre, consisting of the depot and offices at Queens Road, Cheetham Hill, Manchester.

At the time of the tender, the GMA Group did not include a passenger transport operator. As it was considered essential that the successful consortium should include operating expertise, Greater Manchester Buses Ltd (GMBL), a company at present wholly owned by the PTA but subject to future privatisation, was appointed in November 1989. The Consortium, now including GMBL, together with the PTE formed a company with the title Greater Manchester Metro Ltd (GMML), which was incorporated in January 1990 and now forms the operating company. GMML will operate the system under contract to the owner, GMPTE.

A Brief History of Transport in Manchester

The city of Manchester has always been at the forefront of passenger transport. John Greenwood's first British horse bus service of 1824, the Liverpool and Manchester Railway of 1830 with the world's first railway station, the Manchester Ship Canal of 1894 with its unique swinging aqueduct at Barton, and the airfield at Hough End (now Alexandra Park) from where the world's first airline services commenced in 1919 all combined to place Manchester very firmly on the transport map. And now, Greater Manchester's light rail transport scheme, Metrolink, is the first of the new light rail projects, incorporating street running, which are currently being developed in the United Kingdom. As befits the city and the region, Metrolink is in the vanguard of light rail developments and is pioneering much new ground.

From its earliest days Manchester's railway system has suffered from two major problems: the city termini are located at the edge of the city's central area, and there is no direct north-south link. While the rapid growth of the railway system quickly established Manchester's regional and national importance, the number of companies building railways into Manchester, the land areas required for termini, and the lack of flexibility in a central area which was fast becoming built up, all combined to preclude the lines from penetrating further towards the city

Metrolink's LRVs will provide quiet, pollution-free transport, improving the environment for pedestrians, shoppers and office workers alike. This artist's impression shows how the vehicles will blend into the city landscape, in this case Balloon Street looking towards Victoria Station.

centre. Eventually only two main termini remained, Piccadilly, originally opened in 1842 as London Road (serving routes to the south) and Victoria, opened in 1844 (serving routes to the north).

Present day Manchester continues to suffer from these deficiencies of rail communication which were recognised over 150 years ago. Indeed, the first plan to link the sites which were to become Piccadilly and Victoria stations was for a rail tunnel as early as 1839, and a central viaduct link was proposed in 1866. Proposals for a circular 'underground' linking Victoria, London Road, Oxford Road, Central and Exchange stations were made at the turn of the century when London subway building was at its height. Another 'circle' plan appeared in 1912, partly underground with eight city centre stations and a branch to serve the University of Manchester! World War One caused the abandonment of this project and it was never revived.

In the 1920s, Manchester City Council formed an Underground Railway Special Committee, and a system of some fourteen miles was proposed in 1926 which would have covered the city's central area with extensions to Salford, Stretford and Prestwich. A more ambitious scheme of 35 miles was proposed in 1928 incorporating an inner and an outer circle linking the main lines radiating from the points on the edge of the city centre. It was estimated that the inner circle alone would carry 100 million passengers per annum.

Even the legendary Manchester Tramways general manager, Henry Mattinson, produced a scheme combining underground and surface sections with a central interchange near the Town Hall. This scheme provided for connections at the outer ends with electrified suburban lines to enable cross-city services to be operated, a similar principle to today's Metrolink. Nothing came of these schemes, largely due to the costs involved and lack of government grant. Mattinson's scheme died with him later in 1928. At this time the Manchester-Bury line, electrified in 1916, was the only electric line in the city, and the far-sighted Mattinson recommended more. The Altrincham line was electrified in 1931, thus completing the outer routes incorporated into today's Metrolink.

The next proposal came nearly forty years later, in 1966, and this was for a suspended monorail between Middleton and Wythenshawe, linking with Manchester Airport. This was followed by a proposal for a full-size (heavy) rapid transit line linking Ringway with Langley. The intention was to cater for later extensions to include British Rail routes to Bury, Oldham, Hyde, Romiley, Swinton, Eccles, Sale and Altrincham, thus including the present Metrolink route. This ambitious scheme foundered as its predecessors, because of the cost.

The creation of the Passenger Transport Authority and Executive in 1969 led to the proposal in their long-term plan, published in 1973, for a Piccadilly to Victoria tunnel to link suburban lines from Stockport and Wilmslow to Bury and Bolton. This got as far as Parliamentary approval but government funding was not forthcoming and the scheme was abandoned by a newly-elected Greater Manchester Council in 1977.

Meanwhile the one mile gap remained between Manchester's two main railway stations. Latterly, it has been covered by a midibus service which, however, took a circuitous route as it traversed the city centre. Metrolink will finally close this gap, linking the two stations by rail as it runs through from Bury in the north to Altrincham in the south.

WHY
METROLINK?

After the failure in 1977 of the Picc-Vic tunnel proposal to link suburban railway lines from Bury and Bolton to Stockport and Wilmslow across Manchester city centre, this being the last of a long line of unsuccessful schemes for a through north-south rail connection across the city, a Rail Strategy Study was set up in 1982. The participants were the then Greater Manchester Council (abolished in 1986), Greater Manchester Passenger Transport Executive and British Rail. The brief was to consider a wide range of options for the development of the rail network in the Greater Manchester region with particular emphasis on the long-standing problems of poor access to the city's central business area from the two major railway stations and the

For over 140 years it has been necessary to change from rail to road at Victoria and Piccadilly stations before gaining access to the city centre. Metrolink light rail vehicles will provide fast comfortable and convenient interchange facilities and will also accommodate bulky luggage, push chairs and wheelchairs. Journey time between the two railway stations will also be greatly reduced.

lack of a north-south link through the city centre.

Other problems which had developed over the years were the obsolescence of the rolling stock and signalling systems and the outworn as well as non-standard electrification systems on the Bury line (1200v dc 3rd rail) and also the Hadfield/Glossop line (1500v dc overhead). The former Greater Manchester Council had advocated light rail systems in support of its plans for urban concentration, redirection to the inner core, maintenance of the regional centre and conservation of resources and amenities. Furthermore,

British Rail and the PTE had already published proposals for the Windsor Link in Salford to enable trains from Bolton and the north west to reach Piccadilly station, and the Hazel Grove Chord in Stockport to enable trains from Sheffield to run through Stockport to reach Piccadilly and on to Liverpool. These schemes would allow Intercity and Express services to be concentrated on Piccadilly. They were approved in due course, the Hazel Grove Chord opening in 1987 and the Windsor link in 1988.

With regard to the PTE-supported local rail services, the Rail Strategy Study eventually decided upon the light rail option following engineering feasibility studies undertaken by consultant engineers, traffic management studies by the highway authority, and examination of the planning, economic and financial effects. Various forms of light rail and busways were investigated by visits to a number of European cities. Reserved busways and guided busways were considered together with such extraneous options as monorails and automated guideway transit, but the outcome of the Study was that the technical and economic advantages of light rail would provide the most attractive and cost-effective solutions to Greater Manchester's protracted rail problems.

At an overall cost of £112 million for 20 route miles, ie £5.6 million per route mile, Metrolink was seen to be less costly than other comparable systems. The cost of the Tyne and Wear Metro was five times greater, and the cost of London's Docklands Light Rapid Transit system, serving an area with a smaller population than that of the area covered by Metrolink, was costed at eight times greater per route mile.

With its combination of exclusive former British Rail track, reserved street track and priority signalling, Metrolink is intended to improve access into the city centre, provide better links with the British Rail network, improve passengers' journeys both in time and quality, and reduce the level of revenue support for local rail services from the community charge. In addition to combating the two major historical problems associated with Manchester's rail communications, the long-term advantages are expected to include improvement to the environment including additional and extended pedestrian areas, a reduction in vehicular traffic in the city centre, overall financial and economic benefits for the area, encouragement for the development of vacant and derelict land, stimulation of leisure, recreation and tourist facilities, and the creation of new employment opportunities.

Another advantage of the Metrolink system is the potential for extension. Further phases are anticipated which could be a combination of existing suburban railway lines and new lines. An Act of Parliament has been obtained to allow an extension to Salford Quays on the site of the former docks, now a developing business, residential and leisure area. Further Acts will shortly be obtained to cover extensions to Oldham-Rochdale, Rochdale Town Centre, Trafford Park and Didsbury. Powers for Oldham Town Centre are expected in 1992.

Metrolink will complement the network of British Rail services in Greater Manchester in an attempt to provide a fully-integrated transport system incorporating the services of the many bus operators in the region. Metrolink is intended to demonstrate that public transport in the city and its environs can be attractive, convenient and efficient.

THE ROUTE

The first traces of Manchester Metrolink were seen when bus-rail interchanges were opened at Altrincham in 1978 and Bury in 1980. Phase One of Metrolink consists of conversion of the existing British Rail lines from Altrincham Interchange to the southern end of Deansgate, a thoroughfare which leads into central Manchester, and from Bury Interchange to Manchester's Victoria Rail Station. New light rail tracks laid in the city centre connect the two with a spur branching off the line at Piccadilly Gardens to link with a new interchange in the undercroft of Manchester Piccadilly rail station. New Metrolink stations are provided at Victoria and Piccadilly railway stations and at G-Mex, Manchester's major exhibition centre converted from the former Central railway station, closed in 1969. The Piccadilly station interchange will utilise part of the extensive clear area under the wide span of the massive iron columns.

New on-street stations are featured in the city centre and all existing stations between Bury and Altrincham are to be refurbished to a new standard specification making them more attractive and accessible. It is hoped that these major improvements and upgradings will improve the service offered to customers and encourage increasing use of the system.

The Rail Strategy Study assumed that on Intercity lines local British Rail services would continue to be provided by BR with financial support from the PTE. This left a number of lines carrying mainly or exclusively local services for

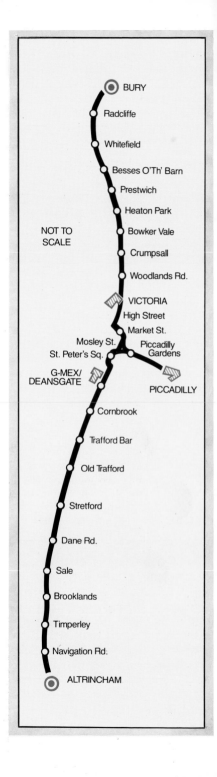

which all or most of the costs would be borne by the PTE. These lines, receiving the heaviest subsidies, would be candidates for closure if severe constraints were to be applied to revenue support and included those from Manchester to Bury, Altrincham, Oldham and Rochdale, Glossop/Hadfield and Marple/Rose Hill. Furthermore, these lines met the criteria set by the study, namely that routes must be capable of segregation from conventional heavy rail routes, they must be compatible with the development of the conventional rail network, existing or potential traffic must justify conversion to light rail, and the routes must contribute to a logical network and afford adequate interchange with the main BR network.

The Bury and Altrincham lines, however, possessed additional commendations. These lines entered Manchester from north and south respectively, they were the busiest lines of those under consideration, and each was outworn and outdated and would require considerable modernisation and re-equipment by BR if they were to continue as heavy rail services.

The route of Phase One of Metrolink thus comprises three sections: the former railway between Bury and Victoria Station, the new city centre sections with a spur in the city centre from Piccadilly Gardens to Piccadilly Station, and the rail alignment from G-Mex to Altrincham, representing a route length of 19.20 miles in total.

The original Bury and Altrincham lines were unlike most other suburban lines in Greater Manchester in that they were constructed primarily to serve local suburban journeys, especially for commuters, and for that reason are perhaps better located in relation to the development in those two corridors. This, no doubt, accounts for the relatively high passenger use which made them ideal candidates for conversion to light rail. The Bury line formed part of the original Lancashire and Yorkshire Railway but for over twenty years it operated independently of the rest of the British Rail network. This absence of interaction with other BR movements made conversion to light rail comparatively straightforward.

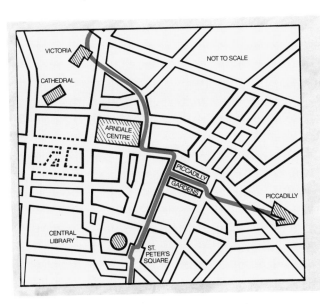

THE CITY
CENTRE SECTION

THE BURY LINE

The Bury to Manchester line was, in fact, the first electric railway in the city. The line was opened in 1879, and electrified in 1916 by the Lancashire and Yorkshire Railway. A third-rail system at 1200v dc was employed which remained unique in British Rail days. Originally a fourth rail was situated between the running rails and bonded to them for the return current but this was subsequently dispensed with.

The original trains built for the system were of all-metal construction and are believed to have been the first of this type not only in Britain but probably in the world. From this modernity in 1916, the two-car EMUs latterly used, of type 504, were built in 1959 and thus were 32 years old at the opening of Metrolink, and time-expired as was the Altrincham line stock. The system, too, had long been regarded as obsolescent. Conversion to 750v dc overhead involved removal of the Bury line's third rail and installation of an overhead catenary system.

The northern terminal of Metrolink is Bury Interchange, opened in 1980, which stands on land formerly occupied by the market and an abbatoir. It was originally conceived as one of the northern terminals of the abortive Picc-Vic scheme and was the only major component to be retained when Picc-Vic was abandoned in 1977. Relatively little change has been necessary to convert it to the northern terminal of Metrolink. This section extends for 9.86 miles from

Bowker Vale station in August 1991. Note the third rail for the BR class 504 stock and the new overhead catenary, then incomplete, for the forthcoming LRVs.

Bury to Manchester's Victoria Station.

From the Interchange, adjacent to the pedestrianised town centre shopping area, the line heads southwards on the original BR tracks through relatively open country, crossing the River Irwell before reaching Radcliffe where extensive park and ride facilities are provided. The line then recrosses the Irwell by viaduct and enters a long cutting to reach Whitefield station with its adjacent bus station.

After leaving Besses o'th Barn, the only intermediate island platform station, the line crosses the M62 Motorway on an unusual concrete structure of inverted T section as it heads for Prestwich and Heaton Park. The line then enters a tunnel from which it emerges to reach Bowker Vale station. Now within the residential suburbs of the City of Manchester, Metrolink passes under Queens Road (where the city's first electric tramcar depot, opened in 1901, was built) near the branch to the depot for the whole system, which is located on former BR sidings. A crossing of the River Irk and a tunnel at Collyhurst bring the line under Cheetham Hill Road bridge and into Victoria Station.

As with the Altrincham section, the nine existing stations required upgrading. All stations on the system will be 'open' with automatic ticket vending machines, public address system and closed circuit TV surveillance monitored from the Control Centre at Queens Road. A new station near is under consideration for Bury South.

Heaton Park station is typical of several on the Bury line where the platforms could only be reached by long flights of steps from the station buildings which are situated at road level. New lifts will be installed at such locations, giving easy access to everyone.

Bowker Vale is one of the stations with the opposite problem but newly constructed ramps, with grades of 1 in 20 or less, will make it easier to reach the LRT system. Metrolink is designed to be accessible to some 95% of the adult population.

THE CITY CENTRE

Traffic congestion has been a problem in Manchester city centre for most of this century. There are photographs of Market Street traffic at a standstill going back to the beginning of the century. Rail vehicles in the form of electric tramcars were no solution in their day as progress on fixed lines was easily blocked by other traffic notably slow-moving horse-drawn vehicles. The Rail Strategy Study defined a three-leg light rail route linking Victoria Station, the G-Mex Exhibition Centre and Piccadilly Station, partly segregated from other traffic, which would form the hub of a new light rail network.

Emerging from Victoria Station the line from Bury now crosses Corporation Street into Balloon Street, crossing Dantzic Street to Snow Hill which formed the only area of significant demolition on the first phase of the system. The design allows a platform to be erected at this location if required by any future development. The site would also provide an interchange for the Arndale Bus Station on the opposite side of Shudehill. Proceeding to High Street, the tracks run in the roadway, being segregated from other traffic. A city centre platform is provided adjacent to Debenhams store. The tracks then swing into Market Street, past Lewis's store, where there is another platform, to the triangular junction at Piccadilly.

Remarkably little property demolition was needed to allow Metrolink to penetrate the key areas of the city. Snow Hill, below, was the major exception and the listed Castle and Falcon public house stands isolated and sheeted against the elements in all its glory.

The spur to Piccadilly Railway Station leaves the triangular junction to run alongside Piccadilly Bus Station with an island platform to provide an interchange with the large number of services stopping there. The line then crosses Portland Street, past the PTE headquarters, and into Aytoun Street where there is an emergency crossover. The tracks then swing south eastwards, across vacant land and into London Road, where they cross the main traffic flow under signal control to gain access to Piccadilly Railway Station Undercroft opposite the junction with Whitworth Street. The Undercroft is linked by escalator to the BR mainline concourse.

The third leg of Metrolink's city centre section leaves the Piccadilly Gardens triangle to run down Mosley Street which is closed to vehicular traffic except for northbound buses. The tracks reach the station in St. Peter's Square adjacent to the Cenotaph, the Central Library and Manchester Town Hall Extension. Crossing the Oxford Street/Peter Street junction, the route runs along Lower Mosley Street, passing the Holiday Inn Crown Plaza Midland Hotel, then leaving the roadway to join the specially constructed ramp viaduct alongside the G-Mex Exhibition Centre. It crosses Great Bridgewater Street by means of the striking new bowstring bridge before proceeding along the G-Mex car park to a new Metrolink station at the end of a footbridge which links with Deansgate Railway Station. Metrolink then uses the southerly of the two former Central Station approach viaducts, which were closed in 1969, to reach Cornbrook Junction burrowing under the BR line in a custom-built £6 million underpass, before rejoining the re-aligned existing track formation to Altrincham. The G-Mex to Victoria Station link covers 1.23 miles and the spur from Piccadilly Gardens to Piccadilly Railway Station 0.45 miles, making a total city centre track length of 1.68 miles.

Piccadilly Undercroft will provide the perfect interchange point between Metrolink and the InterCity network but the cost of creating this facility will greatly exceed the £2 million originally estimated because British Rail's requirements meant a complete redesign. It is scheduled to come into use in June 1992 after major works, including provision of concrete protection barriers for the columns supporting the main line station, and installation of lifts and escalators, are completed.

THE ALTRINCHAM LINE

The line from Altrincham Interchange to G-Mex Exhibition Centre forms the southern section of Metrolink covering a distance of 7.66 miles. The route dates back to 1845 when it was authorised by the Manchester, South Junction and Altrincham Railway Act, the line being opened in 1849. The local company became jointly owned by the LMS and LNER, and it was the latter which carried out the electrification using the 1500v dc overhead system. The electrified line opened in 1931 with new rolling stock comprising three-car sets built by Metro-Cammell. In 1971 the line was converted to 25kV ac operation which enabled British Rail to run its standard three-car EMUs of types 303 and 304. These units were built in 1959 and were therefore life-expired when Metrolink commenced.

For Metrolink the Altrincham line was converted to 750v dc, making maximum use of the existing overhead equipment. This work was undertaken by Balfour Beatty which carried out the original electrification in 1931 and also the conversion to 25kV in 1971. From Cornbrook Junction to G-Mex the new tracks along the viaduct, which once served Central Station, required the erection of an auto-tension catenary system. This changes to a pole and trolley wire system and grooved rail for running along the city streets. There are, in fact, three parallel viaducts approaching G-Mex, the southerly line being used by existing BR services, the central viaduct used by Metrolink, and the presently disused northern viaduct.

At Cornbrook Junction a fly-under takes the Metrolink tracks beneath a re-aligned Warrington line before rejoining the original Altrincham route. Trafford Bar (formerly Old Trafford) station serves an 'edge of city' residential and commercial area, and

The stretch of railway line running along the viaduct from Piccadilly station to Cornbrook is amongst the most heavily used in Greater Manchester. Metrolink cars will travel through the city instead of using this viaduct and the extra capacity thus available for main line passenger and freight trains will be welcomed by British Rail and especially its passengers using the busy platforms 13 and 14 at Piccadilly station.

Old Trafford (formerly Warwick Road) station serves Lancashire County Cricket ground and Manchester United Football ground. The line then runs parallel to the Bridgewater Canal through Stretford for much of its journey to Altrincham, crossing over the River Mersey and under the M63 Motorway. Existing stations at Dane Road, Sale, Brooklands and Timperley link these residential areas to Manchester city centre.

South of Timperley there are two parallel single lines, one for Metrolink and one for BR. This is necessitated by the restricted alignment width between Deansgate Junction, where the BR line from Stockport joins the Metrolink alignment and Navigation Road. There are level crossings at Deansgate Lane and Navigation Road. South of Navigation Road reinstatement of two former goods loops provides a four-track formation enabling both BR and Metrolink to revert to double-track working. The line then passes under the A560 road to reach Altrincham Interchange, a four-platform station which remains in BR ownership, with two platforms for the heavy rail service between Stockport and Chester and two platforms for Metrolink. The latter are adjacent to the bus station in the former station courtyard which forms part of the interchange. This was the PTE's first major bus/rail interchange when opened in 1978.

The nine existing stations on the line required refurbishing, and conversion where necessary to make them more open and accessible, being painted and signed in Metrolink corporate standard design. A new station at Cornbrook has been proposed with a view to future developments in the area, and the possibility of a new station at South Brooklands is being investigated.

The bus/rail/Metrolink interchange at Altrincham will bring central Manchester within reach of a wide catchment area. Interchange with British Rail at Deansgate, Piccadilly and Victoria Stations, with the bus network in Piccadilly Gardens, and access to the main shopping and commercial centres, will ensure the service's popularity.

CONSTRUCTING THE METROLINK

Once Government approval had been obtained for the scheme in 1989, work was able to begin. Although Treasury finance was not immediately forthcoming it was necessary to start work as soon as possible to meet the very tight deadlines involved. A particular constraint was a commitment to city shopkeepers to reopen any roads which had been closed for construction work in order to allow Christmas shopping to proceed as usual. Since approval to proceed was not given until September and the deadline for temporary reinstatement was mid-November it will be appreciated that there was no time to be lost.

The design of the system to meet the PTE's requirements and to comply with the various contracts had been entrusted to W. S. Atkins who have worldwide experience of light rail and had worked with the principal members of the Consortium on previous contracts including the Docklands Light Railway in London.

Work began in a number of locations using different disciplines and equipment according to the particular requirements. Many sub-contractors were employed and the local economy benefitted from the involvement of many companies based in the north west.

Because the three sections of the system had different requirements the work involved varied considerably as will now be seen.

CONVERSION OF THE BURY LINE

Construction work on the former BR Bury Interchange to Manchester Victoria line was necessarily more complex because of the unique nature of the 1200v dc third rail side contact system. Conversion to 750v dc included the dismantling and removal of the third rail, erection of masts and catenary, stringing of the running wire, installation of power supplies together with substations and renewal of the signalling to Metrolink standard. As with the Altrincham railway line, communication troughs have been installed alongside the track for both Metrolink use and with a view to possible commercial use in the future as a source of income generation.

Relatively little change was necessary to convert Bury Interchange to the northern terminal of Metrolink. From this interchange with local bus services the line uses part of an old rail alignment under Manchester Road to join the former line to Bolton Street at Bury South Junction which gave access to the Bury Electric Motive Power Depot. Part of the land made available is intended for the construction of a new park and ride station to be called Bury South, located to the south east of the former depot.

British Rail also required very high levels of protection within Victoria Station. Some of the massive concrete barrier can be seen here in course of construction.

Relatively late in the proceedings an additional overbridge was constructed to allow rail access from the BR network via Heywood to the privately-owned East Lancs Light Railway, currently operating from Bury to Rawtenstall.

As the Metrolink line approaches the city centre it passes under Queens Road where the depot lead is provided to the newly-constructed depot on the site of the former BR Queens Road sidings.

At Victoria Station the former BR line from Bury terminated in platform 5. For Metrolink the line was re-aligned further north towards platforms 7 and 8. New construction enables it to swing southwards to emerge from the station and join the street track, crossing Corporation Street into Balloon Street.

Following a review of safety requirements on its own system, BR required substantial protection to be provided around the columns supporting the roof structure. A further requirement was the creation of a barrier behind the Metrolink platforms which would prevent any derailed LRV which might — in circumstances one cannot imagine — mount and cross the platform and then foul the BR running lines.

Services from Manchester Victoria ceased on 13th July 1991, terminating thereafter at Crumpsall, and thus allowing the major conversion work to be finalised. Complete withdrawal of the third rail class 504 units took place on 17th August 1991, only two weeks short of the line's 112th Anniversary. A rail replacement bus service then operated whilst contractors took possession of the railway line to effect the necessary conversion and upgrading.

More work was necessary than had been expected and included some bridge strengthening. This additional work

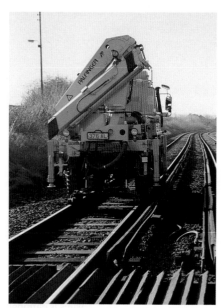

Balfour Beatty used this Unimog — a road/rail vehicle with retractable metal wheels — to transport men and materials on the Bury line

Radcliffe station incorporates extensive park-and-ride facilities; others will be created as Metrolink becomes established.

precluded re-opening of the line as scheduled.

As with the Altrincham line, the nine existing stations required conversion for light rail operation. They were refurbished to Metrolink standard in order to make them more attractive and accessible. Detailed surveys were undertaken with regard to structural condition and relating to the requirement of the PTA to make the stations accessible to an increased percentage of the population. As the Bury (and Altrincham) Interchange was developed earlier by the PTE, little constructional work was required but varying amounts of work were needed at all the other stations. Level access zones were provided at all stations. In some cases lifts were installed and access ramps built. All stations are provided with shelters. Fencing, lighting and signing to Metrolink standard was included in the constructional work carried out by Consortium member John Mowlem & Co plc and its sub-contractors.

CONSTRUCTION OF THE CITY CENTRE SECTION

A number of options for the city centre route was considered in the Rail Strategy Study. Having examined all the relevant factors, particularly the effect that light rail operation would have on other traffic movements including those of buses and pedestrians, the present route was defined. From the demise of the Greater Manchester Council in 1986 the City of Manchester had once again become the highway authority after twelve years, and liaison was maintained with the City Engineer's Department from that time.

A significant aspect of the city centre construction concerned the public utilities: electricity, gas, water and telephone, the underground pipes and cables of which would be affected by the route of the track. Work to the value of £7 million has been carried out on diversion and strengthening of these services which was programmed and co-ordinated by a series of consultation groups representing the PTE, the Highway and Planning Authorities, the Police and the statutory undertakers. These groups were set up in February 1988 and relocation work commenced in March 1989, enabling key areas to be released for track bed construction in accordance with the main construction programme.

To avoid future costly and disruptive repair works to the pipes and cables of the statutory undertakers beneath the

When work began on moving services away from the line of Metrolink's tracks it was a foretaste of major upheavals to come. City Engineers are confident this preparatory work will prove to be a wise investment in avoiding delays to LRT services in the future. This was the scene in Piccadilly, by Tib Street, in September 1989.

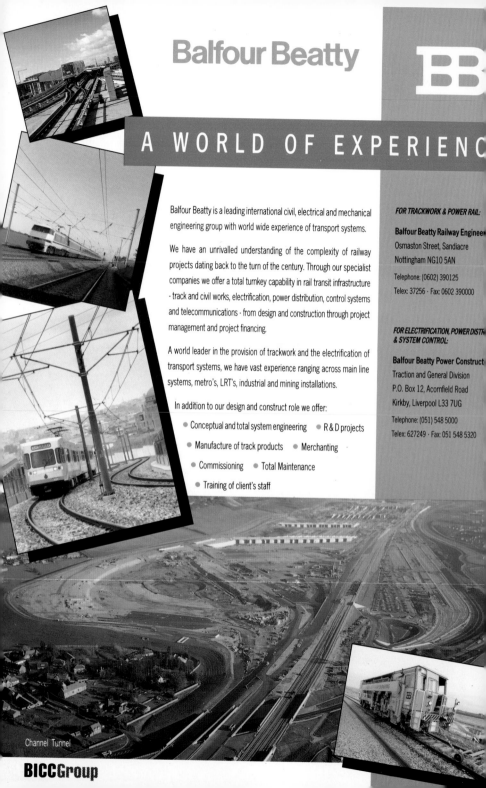

Balfour Beatty

BB

A WORLD OF EXPERIENC

Balfour Beatty is a leading international civil, electrical and mechanical engineering group with world wide experience of transport systems.

We have an unrivalled understanding of the complexity of railway projects dating back to the turn of the century. Through our specialist companies we offer a total turnkey capability in rail transit infrastructure - track and civil works, electrification, power distribution, control systems and telecommunications - from design and construction through project management and project financing.

A world leader in the provision of trackwork and the electrification of transport systems, we have vast experience ranging across main line systems, metro's, LRT's, industrial and mining installations.

In addition to our design and construct role we offer:

- Conceptual and total system engineering   ● R & D projects
- Manufacture of track products   ● Merchanting
- Commissioning   ● Total Maintenance
- Training of client's staff

Channel Tunnel

BICCGroup

on-street track sections of Metrolink, it was decided to strengthen or renew all services which crossed the track for a distance of one metre on each side. It is of interest to note here that the provision of the Tramways Act of 1870 remains in force which defines the area of road which is the responsibility of the tramway operator as the width of the track plus eighteen inches on each side of the track. Some longitudinal services have been rerouted clear of the tracks and several side-entry manhole chambers have been created to allow access to existing sewers. Carrying out these works as a direct contract by the PTE with the statutory undertakers enabled the trackwork within the city

The track base takes shape with shuttering in position above the blinding layer, and the metal mesh laid over concrete spacer blocks. Note the service pipes crossing the trackbed.

centre to progress with minimum disruption. The bulk of this work was completed before the main contract began in December 1989.

With particular relevance to the city centre an important factor of both construction and operation of Metrolink is traffic management. Manchester City Council dedicated areas of highway on the route to the sole use of the light rail vehicles. By a judicious adjustment of traffic flows on various streets, and by highway improvements, the traffic flow will be maintained after the opening of Metrolink. During the construction phase a Traffic Management Group representing all interested parties met weekly to discuss temporary solutions to traffic problems in the city centre produced by the work being carried out at the time. Once decisions had been reached, the PTE informed the press and users of all affected premises.

With the installation of traffic management, work was able to commence on the track laying. The sub-contract for the city centre track laying was awarded to Balfour Beatty Railway Engineering Ltd.

The average depth of the foundation for the rails is approximately 0.5m. below the existing road surface. The first operation was to break out the existing roadway and excavate the underlying road construction. The excavation was bottomed-out and a thin layer of blinding concrete placed to form a clean working surface. Steel reinforcing mesh was then placed on top of the blinding and spaced with concrete blocks to provide top and bottom mats of reinforcement. The steel mesh not only provides structural support for the overlying track but also acts as a conductor drawing off stray current induced by the movement of the light rail vehicles above. The track bed foundation was cast to a level below the foot of the rail. The final level control on top of the track bed foundation was achieved by placing a latex sand and cement screed to a level just 25mm. below the base of the rail. The screed has been developed as a practical solution to what would have been an extremely difficult task of casting concrete to a high degree of level tolerance within the city centre.

The track bed foundation was developed by the contractors in the light of experience from a first stage comprising a level concrete base to a Mark 1 version with a shallow ridge to the outside of each rail. A 'second pour' created the Mark 2 version with more substantial outside ridges, and this became the Mark 3 trackbed foundation with the addition of smaller channels in the track bed.

With completion of the screed laying, the next process was the rail laying proper. The rails, manufactured in Luxembourg, are of grooved section, 18m long, weighing approximately one tonne per length. Delivered as straight section, they were bent on site, in both planes, by special machinery. Once lined and levelled, the rails were embedded in a polymer adhesive and filler which maintains track geometry without tiebars and provides a resilient support for the track. Consequently it insulates against noise, vibration and electrical leakage. This expensive process is of German origin and Metrolink is its first application in Great Britain. The polymer is pourable but is particularly intolerant to differences in temperature and humidity. For this reason the initial polymer installation had to be carried out under cover and in a dehumidified environment.

After considerable difficulty with the original material whereby Manchester's characteristic humidity prevented the polymer from setting, it was decided to change to the Dutch Edilon system which has now proved satisfactory. Delays in this area were the main reason

The trackwork for Metrolink is substantial as this picture shows. Between the rails a light metal framework forms the retaining wall for the polymer fixing.

30

for the lack of progress in reinstating the road surface in Snow Hill, High Street, Mosley Street and Lower Mosley Street.

The rails were welded together by the Thermit process, again using German materials, in the same way in which the original tramway rails were welded at the turn of the century. The track bed foundation was shaped to receive the points which were inserted as pre-fabricated units ready for connection. These had been manufactured at Balfour Beatty's Sandiacre works.

Banks of underground ducts are positioned alongside the trackbed foundation, within the swept path, to take the signalling and power cables. At least 21 channels are available of which Metrolink at present uses six, and the City Engineer's Department uses one for traffic light control which is linked to a computer in the PTE headquarters in Magnum House, Portland Street, in the city centre. There is thus ample provision for any future cables for other purposes which could provide a source of revenue from rental charges.

Communication and draw pits are positioned every 50m. along the track and have, wherever possible, been sited outside the swept path of the rail vehicles. Signal cabling links the system automatically with the operations centre and depot at Queens Road.

Alongside the track, cabinets house the electrical equipment which picks up impulses from approaching LRVs and sends the appropriate command to the point motors where a change of direction is required.

Infilling and surface macadam reinstated the road surface which is now available for both Metrolink and road vehicle use. The city centre section includes varying degrees of segregation, from street running with other traffic to private right of way, with intermediate categories of partial segregation where the alignment is shared with local buses or local access traffic.

The 'black gold' polymer is poured into the cavities to bond the rails to the concrete trackbed. Some £1 million will have been spent on this material which will electrically insulate the rails, and also reduce noise and vibration.

Concrete is pumped to the exact place it is needed — here Mowlem's men are preparing the track base ready for Balfour Beatty to lay the crossing in Aytoun Street.

Work proceeding in Mosley Street with newly erected poles standing alongside the station platform (in shadow lower right).

June 1991 and the delta crossing outside Lewis's store takes shape. The branch to Piccadilly Gardens station and the InterCity station interchange diverges here.

City centre construction work included highway improvements which were carried out under separate contract between the PTE and Consortium member John Mowlem & Company PLC. These improvements consisted largely of road widening and alteration of junction layouts.

The 750v dc overhead line equipment is an unearthed system with either double insulation or reinforced insulation insulators with electrical characteristics which are far in excess of Metrolink requirements. These configurations comply with the prime power system objectives of minimising electrolytic corrosion of public services by stray currents and, in addition, the appearance of the street equipment is enhanced since the use of overhead earth wires is eliminated.

The city centre section is subject to very stringent safety and aesthetic requirements. A fixed-termination trolley wire system with twin wires is employed together with extensive use of synthetic rope for insulation. Metal poles to a total height of 7.5m. support the bracket arms which suspend the running wires at a nominal height of 5.5m. above the road surface. Nominal height on the railway section is 4.7m. but the pantographs on the vehicles will cope with maximum and minimum wire heights of 6.5m. and 3.9m. respectively.

The construction of six stations or platforms was required on the city centre section, excluding the Victoria and Piccadilly interchanges. The city centre stations are of the side platform type except for Piccadilly Gardens which is of the island platform type. G-Mex station has staggered platforms facilitating passenger movements between BR's Deansgate station (formerly Knott Mill) and the G-Mex Exhibition Hall. St. Peter's Square has traditional parallel platforms. Mosley Street, Market Street and High Street stations consist of a single platform serving one direction only for reasons of available space.

Major requirements of the design of the city centre stations were that they

The first opportunity to check the trackwork and clearances came on September 15th 1991. After a preliminary run with the SPV, starting at 4am, the first LRV was pulled through the streets. Everything went according to plan in the 12-hour session. Here the LRV negotiates the delta junction en route to St. Peter's Square.

should be as unobtrusive as possible and ensure maximum accessibility for the disabled. To meet the first-mentioned requirement, these stations have not been provided with buildings. Station equipment is sited in the basements of adjacent buildings. To be as accessible as possible for the disabled the platforms are provided with a raised section at one end, approached by ramps, to provide level access to certain doors of the light rail vehicle. The remaining area of the platform provides access to the vehicle by the use of automatically-operated retractable steps incorporated within the design of the vehicle. Platforms are generally two metres wide and the two levels of platform are connected by a ramp at a nominal 1:20 gradient. Platform height is 915mm above rail level at the high level and 450mm at the low level.

The on-street stations or 'profiled platforms' are thought to pioneer the availability in the UK of the same public passenger transport to both the disabled and the able-bodied.

The tracks are constructed 150mm below street level at the city centre platforms thus reducing the low platform height to about 300mm above pavement level. Platforms incorporate a central information area including ticket vending machines, route maps, signs and clocks.

The distinctive and attractive shelters are supplied by the French company J. C. Deceaux and will be maintained, cleaned and repaired under contract. Each station will be cleaned daily and the shelters will be cleaned every ten days.

The third major construction project

The components for the delta junction were manufactured at Balfour Beatty's Sandiacre plant. The various sections were pre-assembled to ensure everything would fit when final assembly took place on site. This is Mosley Street with the junction to Piccadilly Gardens swinging off to the right.

on the Altrincham line in addition to the Cornbrook Junction underpass and the refurbishment of Cornbrook viaduct, was the building of the G-Mex viaduct. It is dealt with here as it leads into the G-Mex station which is regarded as part of the city centre construction although it is on the edge of the city centre. This wholly new structure carries Metrolink from Lower Mosley Street to the existing podium structure. After crossing the Oxford Street/Peter Street junction the tracks run along Lower Mosley Street, alongside the Midland Hotel crossing Windmill Street, then leaving the

The ramp viaduct climbing from Lower Mosley Street is constructed from reinforced concrete. It was subsequently faced with brick to harmonise with the G-Mex building. Attention to detail in this area has produced what is without doubt the finest feature of the whole street section.

highway alignment to join the new ramp viaduct alongside G-Mex to reach the high level structure across Great Bridgewater Street to the south of G-Mex.

The new viaduct can be broadly divided into three sections. The northern section, from Lower Mosley Street Street to Great Bridgewater Street, runs parallel to G-Mex and is a multispan structure about 120m. in length. The central section spans Great Bridgewater Street and is in the form of a single bowstring arch girder bridge of 44m. length. The third, southern section is 70m. long and is similar to the northern section over much of its length. Construction of the viaduct required the provision of a new retaining wall running its full length. The viaduct itself and the new retaining wall are formed of reinforced concrete. In order that they

should blend with the existing brick structures it was a requirement of the contract that the surfaces should present a brick appearance. To this end brick cladding was applied subsequent to the casting.

The steel bowstring arch bridge crossing Great Bridgewater Street has been designed to reflect its surroundings. The diamond shape of the roof lights of the G-Mex building has been repeated in the arch of the bridge and the square section of the box arch has been turned on its side to present a diamond shape. This bridge, like others on the system, is painted in Metrolink's striking and attractive aquamarine colour scheme.

The abutments are designed in a manner similar to the pilasters of the G-Mex viaduct. The pourable polymer system has been used for securing the rails on the bridge. This reduces noise which is specially important on bridges of this design and especially so at this location with the G-Mex Exhibition Hall and forthcoming Hallé Concert Hall located immediately adjacent on either side.

This major construction project was carefully devised to be sympathetic in design with the Victorian brick structure of the original Central Station. It complements the listed building, and the design of both the ramp and the bowstring arch bridge was approved by the Royal Fine Arts Commission. Manufacture and assembly was carried out by the Belgian company Victor Buyck of Ghent.

A notable landmark in the city is the fine bowstring bridge, erected by its Belgian manufacturers in April 1991. It will enable Metrolink cars to cross Great Bridgewater Street en route to the former railway viaducts leading to Cornbrook and on to Altrincham.

CONVERSION OF
THE ALTRINCHAM LINE

The conversion of the line from Altrincham Interchange to Manchester is the one section of the three sections in the first phase of Metrolink which required the least change as far as the track and method of current collection was concerned. The BR track and catenary system was already in situ and was compatible with light rail transit. Construction work was largely concerned with conversion of the electrical current from 25kV ac to 750v dc and installation of separate LRT signalling. An early complication was that part of the Altrincham line carried diesel multiple units on the BR route between Manchester and Chester. However, from May 1989 these services were diverted to use a freight line between Altrincham and Stockport.

While the track and overhead system was relatively straightforward to prepare, the Altrincham line into Manchester required four major items of construction work: the creation of a turnback siding immediately south of Timperley station, an underpass at Cornbrook Junction, the complete refurbishment of Cornbrook viaduct and the construction of the G-Mex viaduct — which is dealt with under 'Construction — City Centre'. The new underpass was necessary to separate the BR 25kV ac overhead line from Manchester Piccadilly and Oxford Road to Warrington from the 750v dc Metrolink line. Metrolink passes under the BR line and the design work allows for the proposed extension to Salford Quays and Trafford Park to be

The Cornbrook underpass will allow Metrolink's LRVs to pass below the British Rail line from Manchester to Warrington and Liverpool. Work began in the Summer of 1990 and the project was completed and ready for track to be laid by April 1991. Until they are withdrawn in January 1992 Altrincham line trains will continue to use the BR tracks seen centre to right in this view.

An Altrincham-bound train approaches Cornbrook Junction whilst to the left tracklaying for Metrolink proceeds on the adjoining viaduct. This is the point at which the ramp from the Cornbrook Underpass joins the viaduct leading to G-Mex. The lower illustration, taken from the G-Mex car park, shows the viaducts as they were in 1990 before refurbishment began.

constructed without further major structural work at this point. This underpass was the one major constructional project which was not carried out by members of the GMA Consortium. The work was carried out by Shand Civil Engineering Contractors on behalf BR with a contract value of £6 million.

Cornbrook viaduct was originally built between 1876 and 1878 as part of the Midland Railway, and carried two lines into the former Central Station. Despite its name, this station, like the others in Manchester, was on the edge of the city centre. The approach was increased by a further three lines in the 1890s when a new viaduct was constructed to the northern side of the railway leading into the Great Northern Railway's goods station. From 1969 the Cornbrook viaduct was disused with little or no maintenance work being subsequently carried out. As a result the metal sections had become corroded and the brickwork had decayed. The GMA Group carried out an extensive repair programme including the replacement of one metal-deck bridge. This viaduct is unusual in that it divides into two independent structures at which point Metrolink uses the southern portion.

Construction work on the nine existing stations on the Altrincham line included disabled access by the provision of new or modified access ramps and, where ramps were not appropriate, the installation of lifts. Use of these will be monitored from the Control Centre.

Station bridges, retaining walls and platforms were brought up to standard, and the construction work also included the provision of new ducts and building services and new prefabricated buildings or the modification of existing buildings to suit the requirements of LRT passengers. At the same time fencing and lighting was upgraded and Metrolink standard signing was introduced, together with the installation of public address and information display systems.

Castlefield is an area which has benefitted enormously from urban redevelopment — its former derelict buildings and dismal canalscape are being transformed through the Central Manchester Development Corporation. Work is in hand behind the sheeting shotblasting the Metrolink viaducts as an Altrincham train traverses the lower viaduct. The narrow boat is about to leave the Bridgewater canal and enter the lock giving access to the Rochdale canal.

THE VEHICLES

The specially-designed and purpose-built Metrolink vehicles have been constructed by the Firema Consortium in Italy. Firema offered the best overall package in a competitive tender.

Each vehicle consists of two similar cars connected by an articulation unit supported by the centre bogie. By this means the 29 metre long vehicle can negotiate a minimum radius of 25 metres, necessary for some of the sharp curves in the city, particularly those into and out of Market Street and High Street.

Because the cars will have to cope with two quite different boarding situations — on-street and from the existing railway station platforms — much thought was given to the best and most appropriate design. A further and very important requirement was to provide access for disabled persons in wheelchairs, and also for passengers with children in pushchairs or with heavy luggage.

Whilst a low-floor design would have made entry from the street easy for everyone, the existence of the 18 railway stations precluded this. It was finally decided to construct small stations in the city streets at key locations, and to arrange for a section of these station platforms to be at the same height as the railway station platforms.

The vehicles incorporate thermo-statically-controlled heating and fan-assisted ventilation, with fluorescent lighting and ventilation ducts recessed into the ceiling. Hopper-type opening sections are fitted at the top of the main saloon windows. Two emergency communication panels are provided in each car and by this means contact can be made with the driver. Opening and closing of the doors is under the driver's control but the opening of individual

Friday August 30th 1991, and the first vehicle stands outside the Metrolink headquarters awaiting off-loading.

doors is initiated by passengers pressing a push button. This also activates the retractable step if it is required.

The nominal capacity of each articulated car is 201, of whom 86 are seated (4 in fold-down seats). In high-peak conditions 270 can be carried at a density of 6 m² sq. Research using existing traffic loadings together with projected traffic patterns enables Metrolink's planners to predict that no passenger should have to stand for more than 15 minutes outside the city centre on any journey. Should these figures be exceeded the Passenger Transport Executive, who, as owners, will monitor the system, will require changes to be made or impose penalties. It is a part of the philosophy that passengers should be able to stand in the vehicle, if need be, whilst travelling to or from their destination, rather than standing at the station waiting for a train running to a less frequent timetable.

Because the height, degree of slope and general appearance of the on-street station platforms was recognised as being critical if the objectives of maximum access and aesthetic appeal were to be achieved, a mock-up was constructed and exhibited during the Autumn of 1988 in the then disused Birchfields Road bus depot. Almost four decades previously the city's last tram had made its fateful journey into this same depot when the original tramway system closed on the morning of January 10th 1949.

In order to assist everyone involved in the project it was subsequently arranged that a prototype body shell would be delivered to Manchester in March 1990. It was set against a profiled platform to a modified design proposed by GEC Alsthom and housed in one of the arches under the main line railway into Piccadilly station. This allowed detailed examination of many aspects of the car's design to be made and also provided a useful forum for discussion with the many interested groups of people who needed or wanted to see the vehicle.

The mock-up car allowed evaluation of the ramped platforms and their access to the vehicle

The two levels of entry or exit are shown in this diagram. The high level area gives direct access whilst the lower level requires the use of the LRV's steps.

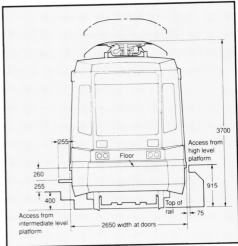

The availabilty of this prototype also helped in other ways. The interior of the cars has been designed in consultation with Metrolink's future passengers, some 2000 of whom visited the prototype during the several open days when it was available to everyone for inspection and comment. Following these most useful events many minor modifications were made in the light of points raised.

Both the interior and exterior of the cars have been designed to give a modern attractive appearance, and yet also to be capable of being easily kept clean and serviced. Design Consultants were involved in this aspect of the cars' design. Fitch RS devised the Metrolink corporate identity and colour whilst Design Triangle developed the livery for the vehicle and the overall styling both inside and out. Modern materials reduce maintenance to a minimum and also meet stringent safety regulations. An automatic car washing plant at Queen's Road will be used to wash every car once every 24 hours and Metrolink's management is determined that the fleet will attract passengers by its clean appearance. The large windows will allow excellent vision for passengers — and they will be kept clean!

Fitting out and wiring the body shells at Firema's Caseralta works. There is sufficient cable in one articulated set to reach from G-Mex to Altrincham and back.

Construction of the cars

The 26 two-car articulated LRVs have been built by the Firema Consortium, under contract to GEC Alsthom (GECA). All five factories in the consortium, which was formed in 1980, have been involved in the work which has been co-ordinated and monitored by project engineers from both Firema and GECA working together. The five factories are located at Bologna, Cittadella, two in Caserta, and Padua.

GECA, in addition to its on-site engineer, also had a team of its electrical specialists at each factory.

The underframe and body construction, fitting out, wiring and completion of the vehicles was divided between the other four factories as follows. All underframes were built at Casaralta, Bologna, where the first eight production vehicles were also assembled and fitted out. Cabs, bodysides and the articulation units were built at Fiore, Caserta, and seven vehicles were finished there. Roofs and the bodyshells were built at Casertane, Caserta (where the prototype had been produced), and seven vehicles were finished there. Four vehicles were completed at Cittadella.

There was thus a considerable amount of movement of partially completed components between factories in the early stages of construction but handling the contract in this manner enabled a greater number of vehicles to be in-build at one time, and was crucial to meet the very tight deadlines.

The bogies for all the 26 cars were constructed and assembled at Officine OMS in Padua, incorporating amongst other items wheelsets and axles from Germany and motors from GECA's factory in Preston.

July 5th and the roll out of the first vehicle, still incomplete, but ready for bogie clearance testing. Metrolink's Operations Director watches progress over the points with a keen eye.

The first vehicle was despatched by road from Bologna on 23rd July. Its journey was not uneventful. Italian and French police held it up during peak holiday times and when it finally arrived on British soil it demolished one of the escorting BMW police cars whilst ably demonstrating the extreme manoeuvrability of its purpose-built trailer.

Following arrival at Queens Road on 29th August the delicate and difficult job of unloading took place next day. A gently sloping ramp had been constructed and brought over on the towing vehicles. The complete vehicle was rolled off the low loading trailer and down the ramp and coupled, via the Dellner coupling, to the Metrolink SPV diesel locomotive. It was then moved into the workshops for commissioning by GECA staff before being handed over to GMML for staff training to begin.

In view of the urgency to get further vehicles to GMML for staff training and

The first vehicle sweeps majestically along the M6, but the escorting Police Range Rover is safely behind one of GEC's cars.

familiarisation, it was decided to air freight at least two further vehicles using the Soviet-built Antonov aircraft which can accommodate two Metrolink vehicles.

General arrangement of an articulated vehicle. Two of these units will be coupled together when required, operated by one driver.

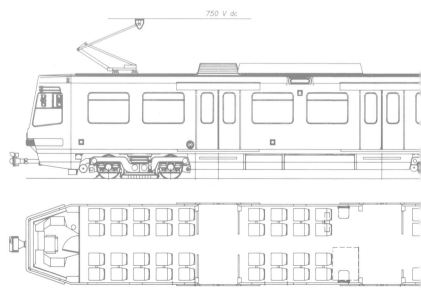

750 V dc

Design of the cars

The basis of the design features a steel underframe upon which is mounted the welded steel body. The wooden floor has an abrasion-resistant rubber covering. Each half of the LRV has fixed seats for 39 passengers, two fold-down seats, together with a further four in the articulation, arranged as shown.

The design life of the cars is 30 years, allowing for major overhaul after ten years. Routine servicing will be carried out every 7 days and will take 5 hours. Each articulated set has cost less than £1m which compares very favourably with the modern LRVs in Grenoble, for example, which have cost over £1.3m each. Albeit the latter cars are more sophisticated than the Metrolink units.

Power is taken from the overhead line via a roof-mounted pantograph manufactured by Brecknell Willis of Chard, Somerset. The pantograph is spring-loaded to maintain contact with the overhead wire and does not need turning at termini.

The LRV is mounted on three bogies, the outer pair each being powered by two 105kw motors, whilst the central non-powered one supports the turntable connecting the two halves of the body via a flexible concertina gangway.

Braking is incorporated on all three bogies. The 48 ton LRVs are designed to accelerate on the flat at a rate of $1.3m/s^2$ when fully laden. This rapid acceleration will assist in maintaining schedules and reducing time lost in any delays to a minimum. Normal braking gives a deceleration rate of up to $1.3m/s^2$ whilst in an emergency the cars will decelerate at an impressive $2.6m/s^2$.

Top speed of the LRVs will be 80km/h (50 mile/h) on the railway sections and 48km/h (30 mile/h) on street.

Braking is effected by a combination of regenerative and rheostatic action, combined with pneumatically operated disc and magnetic track brakes for maximum effect and safety. The precise levels of braking applied from each system are automatically adjusted by the Davies and Metcalfe equipment, and sanding to prevent wheel slip on acceleration or wheel slide on braking is also automatic.

Air suspension will ensure comfortable riding and the bodies incorporate high levels of insulation to keep noise intrusion to an absolute minimum. The bodyshell interiors are sprayed with a sound-deadening material after priming and then most of the inside panelling is further insulated with fibreglass mat in sealed foil bags.

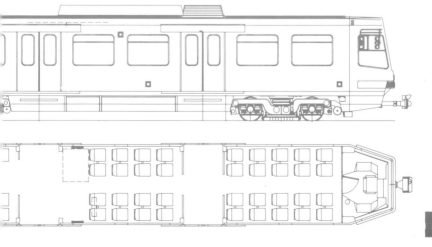

Driving can be performed from either end and the driver has a separate cab which houses all the controls to start and stop the car, operate the door circuits, control the lights and trafficators, activate heating and ventilation, communicate with passengers or the Control Centre at Queen's Road and so on. A deep windscreen and long side windows will give excellent visibility and there are also large self-retracting pneumatically operated mirrors fitted to the outside of the car. These mirrors are electrically heated and are adjustable from the cab.

At the beginning of each journey the driver will program the car's route into the console in the driving cab so that all the necessary points will be automatically set in the correct position, thus avoiding the need to leave the car except in emergency.

The selection and operation of points is handled by a device fitted to the LRV which actuates a transponder set into the road surface ahead of the change mechanism. By this means the points will be changed as the car approaches them and pedestrians will have moved out of the way. It is, of course, the driver's responsibilty to check at all times that the points indicator shows the expected direction, and that the points lie correctly.

To allow maximum flexibility in operation and productivity, the LRVs have been designed to be operated 'in multiple'. By this means one driver will be able to control two (or in emergency up to four) units and the whole operation, including coupling up, will be performed automatically by means of the Dellner auto-coupler fitted to the ends of all LRVs.

Driving the car is achieved by a joy-stick controller which initiates acceleration or braking. A twist-action handle requires the driver to maintain a constant force otherwise an immediate full emergency brake application will be made. This is the universally used 'dead man's handle' system which ensures safety of passengers in the event of the driver being taken ill or otherwise incapacitated.

Access to the cars is through the wide sliding doors, and handrails and stanchions are provided for passengers' convenience. Because the vehicles will have to accommodate two different levels for passenger access, retractable steps are incorporated below each doorway. These steps will extend automatically as required on the trailing vehicles when the cars are in multiple and on-street, the leading vehicle stopping alongside the high ramp for wheelchair access.

On the vehicles two areas adjacent to the centre doors have been specially set aside for wheelchairs and a further two for passengers' luggage. Fold-down seats are also provided in these areas. To assist those in wheelchairs the appropriate area of the exisiting railway station platforms will be specially marked to ensure that they enter by the correct doorway. This is important for those wishing to alight in the city centre where only part of the on-street station is at the LRV floor height.

Tickets will not be sold on the cars, thus leaving the driver free to concentrate on the task of driving. Every station will have a minimum of two ticket vending machines and it will be the passenger's responsibility to see that he or she has a ticket before boarding. On-vehicle checking of tickets will be carried out by a team of Customer Service Inspectors.

Externally the LRVs are finished in an attractive livery of pale grey and dark grey with aquamarine relief bearing the Metrolink logo, fleetname and number. Advertising will be carried.

OPERATION

To ensure that the system functions efficiently, especially in the street sections, the LRVs will be constantly monitored by the Control Centre. The communication systems on the car will feed information through the cables buried beneath the road surface back to the central computer. By this means the duty controller will be able to tell from a VDU display at Queens Road where any LRV is located at any time. By this means running times can be checked at a glance and if delays occur the controller will be able to make the necessary arrangements to keep the service running in the most expeditious manner

Closed circuit television on-street and at the railway stations will also provide monitoring and security.

The heart of the system, and the limiting factor for line capacity, will be the delta junction in Piccadilly. Cars must operate in such a manner as to keep its various crossings free at all times to avoid bringing the whole system to a halt. Because the on-street stations are built to take a maximum of two articulated sets it will sometimes be necessary for drivers to wait before entering stations when multiple operation is taking place.

Approaching certain locations such as the Mosley Street station drivers will have to wait on a designated part of the delta until the previous unit has cleared the platform when two two-car sets follow each other, otherwise the second set will obstruct the tracks leaving Piccadilly Gardens. It is anticipated that a controller will be located at this point to ensure smooth operation, certainly in the early days of the system's life.

Firema supplied a neat ramp to enable the vehicles to be off loaded. Adjustable suspension on the trailer allowed easy vertical alignment and the first vehicle rolled off without a hitch.

Sunday September 15th and the first car makes its historic diesel-propelled trial run with the Railway Inspector in attendance.

Overnight storage of the LRVs will be at Queens Road but during operational hours sets may be held or stored in Millgate Siding Victoria and Piccadilly Undercroft.

The first car made its all-important gauging run through the city in the early hours of Sunday 15th September. It was propelled from Queens Road to Victoria Station where it remained whilst the SPV diesel made an initial run to Aytoun Street and back. The LRV was then propelled to St. Peter's Square where it was again detached whilst the SPV ran to G-Mex and back. Finally both vehicles were taken over the various legs of the delta junction.

The trial was completely successful and all concerned were encouraged that this milestone had been cleared without any major problem.

Following completion of the trials and after consultation between GMML and the PTA/PTE, it was announced that opening dates for the Bury, City and Altrincham sections would be 21st February, 20th March and 17th April respectively.

Frequency of operation has been fixed so that between 6am and midnight Monday to Saturday and 7am until 11.30pm on Sundays and Bank Holidays trains will run every 10 minutes off peak and every 5 minutes in the peak hour (Monday-Friday). Once the Altrincham line becomes operational it will be necessary to revise the method of operation and single cars at the higher frequency will result.

Metrolink's management is eagerly awaiting the opportunity to set the new system in motion. It is confident that its potential passengers will see the advantages and convenience of the new system, and also appreciate the comfort and smooth riding of the new vehicles. No one is complacent however. The long shut down on the Bury line, coupled with innumerable failures during the last few months of BR operation as the life-expired equipment and contractor's JCBs occasionally severed power cables left a legacy of disenchanted travellers. Only by keeping to time and taking advantage of the new equipment and staffing attitudes can they hope to win back passengers who reluctantly found alternative means of transport.

Paradoxically GMML's biggest potential problem is its predicted success! It is anticipated that once people see the advantage of the new system, both as commuter travel in the peak and for shopping and leisure travel off-peak, the numbers of would-be travellers may well outstrip the capacity of the LRVs. The situation will be continuously monitored and Operations Director Scott Hellewell sees this as his biggest challenge since the lead time on further vehicles is not expected to be less than 15 months.

Nevertheless GMML are confident that the time spent on research and development of these initial 26 Light Rail Vehicles will prove to be a good investment for the citizens of Greater Manchester who will, for the first time, have transport comparable to that seen and used by so many travellers to the Continent. They await with eager anticipation the opportunity to expand the system and to bring these benefits to an ever-increasing number of people.

Multiple Operation

An important feature of Metrolink's operation is the ability to couple the LRVs together to work 'in multiple'. By this means capacity can be doubled by joining two vehicles together, and productivity is also increased since only one driver is required to operate two (or more) articulated cars. Coupling and uncoupling is performed solely by the driver, from within his cab.

The means of achieving this is the automatic coupler fitted to the ends of all the LRVs. Joining two units together is accomplished simply by driving one set slowly towards another. As the couplers meet they automatically engage and lock, and a light on the driver's control desk confirms that the engagement has been performed satisfactorily. The coupler incorporates a hydraulically-damped shaft which is pivoted below the driving cab. Coupling is designed to be performed at 5 miles/h or less.

In addition to effecting a mechanical engagement the coupler also connects all the necessary electrical and pneumatic circuits. Thus the driver has full control over the operation in both vehicles of doors, lights, trafficators, indicator blinds, public address system, pantographs, etc. in addition to the more fundamental requirements of supplying power to all motors through a controlled and balanced mode to give surge-free running. Braking is similarly monitored and controlled as are the automatic sanding routines.

The Dellner couplers fitted to Metrolink cars are of a standard pattern with the necessary circuiting to suit GMML's particular requirements. Another benefit of this system is the complete elimination of any visible wiring — jumper cables — between the ends of sets working in multiple. Regular maintenance to ensure trouble-free operation will be part of the weekly routine for the GMML service engineers.

The Dellner coupler

Cities as diverse as London, Caracas, New York, Hong Kong, Toronto and Recife have gained from GEC ALSTHOM's 85 year capability in DC trackside power supply equipment for mass transit and light rail systems.

Comprehensive computer simulation facilities, which aid the design optimisation of the power supply and traction equipment on dc railway systems, are an important element of GEC ALSTHOM's expertise and place us light years ahead of our rivals.

We undertake comprehensive DC trackside power supply contracts which include AC and DC switchgear, transformers, rectifiers, auxiliary equipment cabling as well as AC distribution equipment for works depots, station services, signalling and ventilation. Our skilled project management teams and quality assurance organisation ensure that the best possible service is provided.

DC TRACKSIDE POWER SUPPLIES
LIGHT YEARS AHEAD

1991

GEC ALSTHOM
Transmission &
Distribution Projects
Ltd, PO Box 27,
Stafford, ST17 4LN

Tel: 0785 57111
Fax: 0785 52540

**GEC ALSTHOM TRANSMISSION & DISTRIBUTION
PROJECTS LIMITED**

GEC ALSTHOM

50

THE POWER SUPPLY

Metrolink cars are electrically powered, drawing their current from overhead wires as shown. The contract to design the power supply system and to distribute it was awarded to GEC Alsthom of Stafford.

It was originally envisaged that a line voltage of 750 volts dc would be used on the street-running section where cars run at lower speeds. The more economical 1500 volt dc supply would have been used on the two former railway sections, where speeds of up to 50 miles/h will be achieved.

One of the main advantages of this situation would have been the ability to provide lighter section overhead on the railway sections and also to reduce the number of sub-stations.

Design work and computer simulation with predicted traffic patterns and loadings showed that such a system was feasible. Because the cars will use regenerative braking however, where the motors act as dynamos and feed current back into the system as they slow down, the energy saving would be reduced if the system had been split into three separately fed sections. This factor, and the need to plan ahead for future extensions which would also involve street running finally led to the decision to standardise on 750 volts throughout the whole system. The vehicle's equipment was thus simplified.

Power is supplied by Norweb at either 11kV or 6.6kV depending on availablity in different areas of the city. Ten sub-stations then convert this supply to the 750v dc required to power the cars, and also provide power to change the electrically operated and heated points, the various control systems and the

The twin overhead wires will provide up to 2000 amps at 750 volts to power the LRVs. Substantial poles are needed to cope with the tension of four wires above the two tracks.

back-up battery systems. The Queens Road Control and Maintenance complex has its own sub-station.

The whole power system has been built to be as reliable as possible but takes account of possible failures and also equipment being taken out of service for maintenance.

The return current is designed to find its way back to the sub-station without leakage thanks to the construction of the track base and also the insulation of the street sections by bonding the rails in a plastic polymer. Insulation on the railway sections is achieved in the conventional way by means of wooden sleepers and stone ballast.

GEC Alsthom is confident that the system will cope with the present and future requirements of Metrolink including the use of additional cars when the system is extended partially or to its maximum potential.

QUEEN'S ROAD OPERATION AND MAINTENANCE CENTRE

Metrolink's headquarters, where its offices, control centre, depot, sidings, washing plant and workshops are located, forms an £8 million four-hectare brand new purpose-built complex. This scheme was handled by Consortium member AMEC through its Fairclough Civil Engineering subsidiary. In addition to providing office accommodation for the Company's staff the complex provides all the necessary facilities to service, clean, maintain and stable the fleet of LRVs. Workshops with pits and a wheel lathe and press, are equipped to handle all the necessary tasks.

The headquarters also houses the nerve centre of the whole operation — the Control room.

During the conversion of the Bury line the contractors stored equipment and materials on site, including the works train containing cement mixing and pole drilling equipment. Metrolink's diesel locomotive — the SPV — is based here and will be used, along with a small fleet of road vehicles, to access all parts of the system to meet whatever operational requirements arise.

The complex forms an attractive yet functional base capable of expansion to meet future needs as the system expands.

The maintenance area is spacious and well-equipped, with doors to the north and south, allowing vehicles to pass through the building. The SPV and flat truck are standing on the pit road. A wheel lathe is incorporated in one road, at rail height, allowing turning to take place without removing wheels and axles from the bogies. The business end of the SPV is seen below. The poles (seen below right), are ready for erection. Note that some are cranked, for use where clearances or fixing points are restricted. Balfour Beatty's pole-fixing train awaits its nocturnal trip.

SIGNALLING AND CONTROL

GEC Alsthom Signalling Ltd (GASL) of Borehamwood, Hertfordshire, is the sub-contractor to GMA for the design, manufacture, supply and installation of a new train control and signalling system for Metrolink. Functions affecting signals, vehicles and power distribution are controlled by the Signet central computer system in the Operation Centre adjoining the depot at Queens Road, Manchester, adjacent to the Bury line. The system includes three high resolution colour Visual Display Units complete with keyboard and trackerball which allows the whole Metrolink operation to be monitored and controlled from the Operations Centre.

The controller at Queens Road has a colour map of the System shown on one of the workstation VDUs, from which each vehicle's progress can be observed. There are also detailed maps showing the Altrincham line, the Bury line and the City Centre section with the boundaries at the G-Mex Centre, Victoria and Piccadilly stations, where the street running section commences and different driving rules apply. Trains automatically and continuously identify their positions on a diagram on the screen, thus enabling the controller to observe the whole operation at a glance.

On the segregated, former railway sections, Metrolink is fully signalled by a two-aspect automatic system which incorporates the latest proven Solid State Interlocking (SSI) technology. The controller sets the routes for all train movements in the interlocking areas and can switch certain parts of the System into a limited automatic working mode to ease his workload. Automatic track-circuit block working is used between interlocking sites. A station warning board is positioned at braking distance before each station in the segregated section, and Yellow/Green aspect repeater signals are used where the sighting of the normal Red/Green signal is restricted. An automatic train stop

New two-aspect signalling being installed at Bowker Vale by GASL engineers whilst the BR lookout man stands by.

system stops any train which may pass a signal at red.

The Altrincham and Bury lines have been signalled so that vehicles can be turned at G-Mex and Victoria station, enabling each line to operate a shuttle service should the City Centre section be blocked. The signalling system allows for vehicles to be stabled in sidings at Timperley and Victoria station as well as the platforms at Bury and Altrincham, the headshunt at Piccadilly Undercroft and at the depot. The depot has two leads which will provide alternative entrances/exits to improve operating flexibility. Both leads into the depot are signalled but there is no signalling in the depot itself.

There is a single line section between Timperley and Altrincham and provision has been made to turn vehicles at Timperley. There are emergency-worked ground frames at Whitefield, Crumpsall and Old Trafford providing trailing crossovers for use in emergency which are operated by the driver in conjunction with instructions from the control. The two level crossings in the

single line section on the Altrincham line are under the control and safe operation of the BR signal box at Deansgate Lane, near Navigation Road. The level crossing at Hagside on the Bury line is operated remotely from Queens Road with Closed Circuit Television supervision but can be operated locally by Metrolink staff in cases of emergency.

In the City Centre, from G-Mex to both Victoria and Piccadilly, the driver drives 'on-sight', as would any other road user. Here, he is in sole command and has full responsibility for the safe progress of the vehicle. There is an interface with the road traffic junction signals so that approaching LRVs, detected through transponders and special loops within the tracks, automatically request a proceed aspect so as to improve the flow of LRVs in the city.

Between Navigation Road, below, and Timperley the two railway tracks will be bi-directional. One will carry the Metrolink LRVs replacing the BR class 304 EMUs (as seen here), whilst the other, non-electrified line, will be used by BR for diesel services to Chester and elsewhere.

The question of what type of signals should be used for Light Rail Vehicles was discussed by a Light Rail Transit street running working party made up of representatives of the Railway Inspectorate, the Department of Transport, and traffic signal engineers from Manchester and Sheffield. The design had to be compatible physically and electrically with standard British traffic signals. To add a further red/amber/green head to existing signals would produce an unnecessary clutter of signals. It is also essential that signals should not cause confusion to drivers of normal road vehicles. Even with a distinctive symbol or shape, the use of coloured signals would be potentially confusing, particularly since LRV signals are not familiar to road vehicle drivers.

The preferred solution is a signal quite unlike a normal road traffic signal. White bar symbols are used as LRV signals in several European systems. The Metrolink design uses a white horizontal bar meaning 'stop' and a white vertical bar meaning 'proceed', incorporated into a single signal aspect of 300mm diameter. The vertical bar can be changed to one at 45 degrees to indicate 'proceed left' or 'proceed right'. It remains to be seen whether this Manchester initiative will be adopted by future British systems.

The points in Piccadilly Gardens are automatically set for each vehicle, depending on a route code entered by the driver at the start of each journey into the vehicle's electronic recognition system. Points indicators in the street enable the drivers to check, together with observing the point blades, that the points are set correctly. It is a safety feature of the system that the City Centre points only move just before an LRV reaches them by which time pedestrians will have stepped out of the way of the LRV and the point blades. All points have provision for heating in icy weather.

The complex pointwork in the delta junction in Piccadilly is controlled from a bank of trackside cabinets. These house the electronic equipment to respond to the signal from an approaching LRV and to set the points in the appropriate mode.

Point controlling and operating equipment being installed in Market Street, outside Debenhams. The German equipment is housed, as shown, in a metal casing between the tracks. This unit will control the points leading from Market Street into Mosley Street or Piccadilly Gardens.

The signalling system is covered by a back-up or protected power supply. In absolute emergencies, the driver or operating staff can hand-crank point machines. A key switch on the traffic light controller at each junction can be operated in an emergency to request a phase for the LRV.

Metrolink Control

This is the Operation's nerve centre, manned 24 hours per day, 365 days a year. At busy periods there will be two people in the Control: a Senior Controller and a Controller. Both also have outside duties on the system. The functions of the Control are as follows: Monitoring of the train service; Surveillance of stations; Control of power supplies; Monitoring of TVMs; Supervision of staff; Control of Hagside level crossing.

Monitoring of the train service

The Control Centre will monitor running of the service — to ensure that trains are running to time and, where they are not, to take appropriate corrective action. With nearly 500 departures per operating day such monitoring must be done on a 'by exception' basis. It is therefore assumed that trains are running to time or within pre-determined tolerances unless a Controller observes that they are not or a Driver, Controller or Customer Services Inspector out-on-the-line reports some occurrence or out-of-course running.

If a train is running out-of-course the Controller must decide what action to take. It may be to turn it short, so as to pick up its schedule, or to terminate it. If there is a problem with a train he may take it out of service, summoning up a replacement train, if one is available. The Controller must make the necessary arrangements to alter the Driver's duties to cover such eventualities.

Monitoring services also includes dealing with emergencies. These may be mishaps on the Metrolink system, with an LRV involved in an accident, or may be external, such as a fire in the City Centre. There are direct 'hot' lines to both the Greater Manchester Police and Greater Manchester Fire Brigade Control Rooms. There is also a direct line to BR's Deansgate Junction signalling centre, because it controls Metrolink between there and Altrincham.

All 26 LRVs are radio fitted and Control can call them individually or collectively. Likewise an LRV Driver can call Metrolink Control. Drivers are expected to report lateness (beyond the laid down tolerances) and any untoward incidents.

Surveillance of stations

All 26 Metrolink stations are unmanned but are under CCTV surveillance. They are 'poled' on a regular basis and the picture comes up on one of 14 TV monitors in the Control Room. These monitor the platforms, ticket machines and subways, lifts and escalators, where appropriate. All stations have public address and stations can be called in groups or on an all-system basis. Public address is used only during out-of-course running or when emergencies arise.

On each platform there is a Passenger Emergency Call (PEC) button which enables a passenger to talk direct to the Controller. Pressing this button also brings the relevant camera picture onto the monitor, so the Controller can both see and talk to the passenger. There is also a staff telephone at each of these locations for use by staff who do not have a mobile radio.

Control of power supplies

The receipt of power from Norweb and its distribution over the system both to provide traction power and to power other systems is monitored by Control. Control can isolate any section of Metrolink if the need arises.

Monitoring TVMs

All 69 TVMs are monitored from the Control. If anything goes wrong — from running out of change to complete failure — it is reported so that corrective action can be taken. All TVMs also have a 'molest' alarm in case of their being attacked.

Supervision of staff

All operating staff sign on and off at Control. Although staff duty rosters are known well in advance there may be a need to revise these rosters on an ad hoc basis. Control has to ensure that all trains are provided with a Driver.

Controllers must also liaise closely with Engineering to ensure that all LRVs are cleared daily and that maintenance schedules are kept. When vehicles have to be changed over for any reason it is up to Control to ensure that this has the minimum adverse effect on services.

Control of Hagside Crossing

This level crossing on the Bury line between Bury and Radcliffe is under the supervision of Control. The crossing barriers lower automatically on the approach of the train but the signal protecting the crossing is cleared by the Controller when he can see, through the CCTV monitors, that there is nothing trapped on the crossing. The barriers are equipped with 'auto-rise' and 'second train coming' facilities.

PERSONNEL AND TRAINING

From the outset of the Metrolink proposals staff within the PTE were involved in the conceptual work, liasing where necessary with British Rail and also with the City Engineers and Planners. As the scheme progressed D. Scott Hellewell was to take a major role and when the Tenders were accepted and Contracts let he moved to Queens Road to be on hand as work began. Scott Hellewell had moved back to Manchester in 1988 to become the PTE's nominee to spearhead the new company which would operate the system. A former GMPTE officer, he returned to Manchester from South Yorkshire PTE where he had been Director of Operations, the position he currently holds in Metrolink and which also incorporates responsibility for engineering matters.

At the beginning of 1990, Eric Black joined the organisation as Chief Executive, being seconded from GEC. Eric Black brought with him experience of Mass Transit construction and operation in Hong Kong and also experience of rail vehicle construction at Metro Cammell where he had been Director and General Manager of Projects.

The appointment of Don Kenny, seconded from Mowlem, completed the members of the Directorate. Don Kenny had previously been Commercial Director at London City Airport and joined Metrolink as its Commercial Director.

Miss Hilary Taylor, who had worked with Eric Black at Metro Cammell, joined the team shortly afterwards to look after the administration of the new company and in fact became its first employee.

Jim Harries soon followed to take up the position of Engineering Manager after spending his previous working years with British Rail.

In July 1990 recruitment of the senior management staff was completed when Paul Neal joined the Company as Operations Manager, having gained invaluable experience of rail operations with both London Docklands and the Tyne and Wear Metro.

This small team, together with two secretaries, was fully occupied planning the Company's strategy and staffing requirements and worked from a Portakabin alongside those used by the contractors in an area above the present offices.

In February 1991 the first advertisements appeared in local papers in the Manchester area for staff to join GMML (as the operating company had now become). More than 9000 people applied for the 140 or so jobs on offer and the now slightly expanded team spent many long days — and nights — sorting though the replies. It was necessary to employ a specialist on a temporary basis to assist in the enormous recruitment task and Elwyn Roberts joined as Recruitment Officer.

By now GMML's staff were working from the pagoda-roofed offices alongside the main workshop and maintenance complex, a considerable improvement on the former location on the upper level. Initially access was somewhat difficult but the entrance road with its security cabin was soon completed and the complex began to look as its designers had intended — except for the roof!

Because GMML would have no revenue until operation began, being financed by the Consortia building the ystem, it was necessary to work within ght budgets and yet also to be aware of he short timescale available for staff raining and familiarisation. New echnology often presents minor roblems of course, and Metrolink ound that the vehicles arrived later than hey expected, compounding this ituation.

Some training could clearly be given n-house. Every person joining the ompany goes through an induction ourse at Queens Road and the Directors f the company are actively involved in hese courses to ensure that staff are ware of the exacting standards equired of them in order to promote Metrolink to the travelling public. In a ompetetive environment Metrolink are letermined not to be found wanting in ustomer relations and levels of service.

Specialist staff were sent to the elevant manufacturers for training, nd many visits were made to other ystems in Europe to gain detailed knowledge. Experience gained on some of these visits was to reap considerable benefit, often more than paying for the cost of the visit in immediate savings, in addition to longer term advantage. Because of the high calibre and wide experience of the staff employed it now became apparent that it would be both possible and economically sensible to perform certain functions in the Company's own workshops which would otherwise have been contracted out. This led to the recruitment of a small additional number of employees.

Some aspects required a more structured training progamme which could only be given by another operator with similar routines. Accordingly a team of Senior Controllers and Customer Service Inspectors was sent to Brussels to be trained in the operation of the LRT system. The training package was organised by Transurb in conjunction with STIB (Societe des Transports Intercommunaux de Bruxelles), the Brussels transport operator, and was extremely thorough.

Metrolink staff trained in Belgium spent time on this driver simulator in the training school

The team spent several weeks based at the STIB training school at Haren where their instruction included the use of driver training simulators, theory and practice relating to electrical supply, and all necessary training to meet the safety requirements of exisiting and new UK legislation. They spent many hours driving the on-street trams in passenger operation and qualified as drivers before returning to Manchester to apply their knowledge there. They also spent time in the Control Centre learning how to operate the system and how to cope with problems.

The Brussels-trained operatives will teach these skills to others joining GMML and in this they were to be assisted initially by the man who organised their own training in Brussels Paul Gijselings. Paul came to Manchester for 6 months together with another specialist instructor from STIB Roland De Smet, who spent three months training workshop and maintenance staff at Queens Road.

Metrolink will thus be able to draw on a core of first-hand experience of a very high level of competence to operate it new technologically-advanced system.

The first car awaits the return of the SPV before making its journey to the G-Mex station. Overhead wiring has yet to begin in St. Peter's Square.

FUTURE PLANS

The enormous amount of work undertaken in the city centre to allow Metrolink cars to run through the streets could only have been justified as a part of a wider plan. Although a great number of people will benefit from the new system — up to 10 million people are forecast to use the Light Rail Vehicles in the first year — the Bury and Altrincham to Piccadilly services represent only the first phase.

To give maximum benefit to the greatest numbers of potential travellers a six-line system has been designed around the central street section so that passengers from every part of the proposed network will have access to the interchange in Piccadilly Gardens, the point destined to be the hub. For this reason it was essential that these main arteries should be well-designed and constructed, for the success of the whole system will depend on their satisfactory performance over a period of many years.

It had been intended to build Phase 1a, a line to Dumplington with a branch into the rapidly developing Salford Quays, as soon as construction work on Phase 1 was complete. Indeed, the contracts signed in September 1989 made provision for a 5% discount to be given to the PTE if Phase 1a had been confirmed by December 1990, thus allowing the various contractors to give continued employment to men and equipment.

To the great frustration of everyone concerned with Metrolink it has not been possible to do this and a question mark now hangs over the timing of future phases, and also the order in which they might be built.

In a chicken-and-egg situation the Trafford Park line to Dumplington has fallen foul of Government Planning. When proposals were made for the giant shopping complex at Dumplington it was a Government stipulation that adequate public transport must be provided if planning permission to develop the area was to be given. Accordingly Metrolink planners created Phase 1a to meet this requirement, and also to provide a link to the rapidly developing Salford Quays area which is now becoming home to thousands of office workers but which has no rail link and only relatively poor bus services. The possibility of Manchester hosting the 1996 Olympic Games was seen as another good reason to pursue Phase 1a.

Sadly the Government, several years later, has still made no decision about the development of Dumplington shopping area. Without this shopping area Phase 1a could not be viable, and without the Dumplington line Salford Quays could not be justified because future phases of Metrolink have to be funded without Government money.

The PTE is still discussing with developers the funding of the Dumplington and Salford Quays lines should the economic climate change. It has also completed the evaluation of the case for Section 56 grant for the conversion of the Oldham-Rochdale line — the third element in phase 1a. Other options for extensions are also being studied in the light of the ever changing pattern of transport in the country.

ACKNOWLEDGEMENTS

This publication could not have been completed without the considerable assistance of the many people who willingly spared time to ensure events were recorded correctly. In particular, Scott Hellewell and through him the late David Graham, gave tremendous encouragement and opened many doors.

We are also grateful to Chris Mulligan, Director General GMPTE; Roger Hall Deputy Director General; Bill Tyson, Director of Planning and Promotion. Through them Pat Bromilow, Karen Larkin, Catherine Cairncross, Jane Nierney, Alison Rushton, Tony Young and Geoff Brierley, all at GMPTE.

The Directors of GMML — Eric Black, Scott Hellewell and Don Kenny, and their staff, including Hilary Taylor, Margaret Hyde and secretaries and others who patiently dealt with so many queries!

We also wish to acknowledge the assistance of various individuals from the many companies, including: W. S. Atkins — Roger Hull and Allan Woodgates; Balfour Beatty — Noel Duffy, Steve Pont, Steve Shudall, Bev Waterhouse; Manchester City Engineers Department — Sinclair McLeod and Keith Williams; Faircloughs — Keith Hick; Firema's management and all staff at their Bologna factory; GEC — Geoff Done, Brian Middleton and Mike Scott; GMA — David Cox; Mott MacDonald — David Rumney; Mowlems — Nicholas Hopkins and Jim McDermott; PTA/PTE — Councillors Jack Flanagan and Joe Clarke; Margaret Robinson Photography; STIB — Paul Gijselings and Marc Thienpont; Transmark — John Berry. Mark and Geoffrey Senior spent many hours patiently tracking down items which needed photographing, and Geoff Hyde assisted in many ways, including reading all the proofs. We are indebted to Deryk Bailey for the illustrations on the cover and of Balloon Street. If we have inadvertently omitted anyone we sincerely apologise.

Photography in this handbook has been handled by the following, to whom we record our thanks:
Ray Catterall, W. G. S. Hyde, Manchester City Engineers, Margaret Robinson, G. M. Senior, J. A. Senior, M. D. Senior, Steve Shudall, STIB.